THE ROYAL UNITED HOSPITAL

The Royal United Hospital

A social history 1747-1947

Kate Clarke

Mushroom Publishing

First published in 2001 by
Mushroom Publishing,
156 Southlands, Bath, BA1 4EB.
http://www.mushroompublishing.com

Printed in Great Britain
by Impress Print, Corby.

ISBN 1-84319-039-7

Contents

*Pauper Clinic; City Infirmary; Union with Casualty
Hospital to become Bath United Hospital.*

*Sounds, sights and smells of hospital building; students.
Extension to building and change of name to Royal United
Hospital; Great Western Railway; Widcombe disaster.*

*The need to improve standards; rules; uniform; salaries;
living conditions; Matrons.*

*Admission by ticket; wards; beds; clothing; food and drink;
chapel; patients' library; servants' ward; rules; visiting
times; discharge.*

*Eventual admission as inpatients; children's ward;
tonsillectomy rooms.*

*Election system; some early doctors; residents; relationship
between medical and administrative staff.*

*Porters; surgery boys; dispensers; hospital secretaries;
domestic staff.*

*Smallpox; cholera; water; sewerage; treatments; operating
theatre; anaesthesia; antisepsis; hygiene.*

Introduction

This book tells the story of the Royal United Hospital (RUH) in Bath from its beginnings in 1747 until the introduction of the National Health Service in 1947.

In 1884 it was reported that, due to shortage of space, the earliest records of the hospital had been sold as scrap paper (for which the sum of twenty-seven shillings was received) so there are very few documents covering the first eighty years of its history. Fortunately the minute books of the Management Committee for the years of 1827 onwards were kept and when the hospital moved from the old building in Beau Street the numerous volumes were transferred to the new Combe Park site. When space was limited there in 1987 the minute books and archives, together with other RUH volumes previously kept at the Royal National Hospital for Rheumatic Diseases, were sent for safe keeping to the Record Office at the Guildhall in Bath.

Committee notes for any institution, large or small, often contain much repetition or tedious detail and the RUH minute books are no exception. Yet among the pages there are snippets which make it possible for us to picture the wards and learn something about the conditions for patients and the staff who cared for them.

Entries in the later volumes show how social changes in Bath affected the RUH and they also show the efforts made by local people to maintain it as a voluntary hospital before the introduction of the National Health Service.

The majority of quotes in this book are from the minutes and are not specifically referenced. However, enough dates have been given for future researchers to find the relevant entries.

1

Beginnings

Newcomers to Bath who need to find their way around the Royal United Hospital will see a varied collection of buildings, some modern and others obviously sixty or seventy years old. But there is no indication that the history of the hospital goes back to 1747, the date when a charity was formed to provide medical treatment for destitute people in the city. To explain how this small effort evolved to become the present hospital, it is necessary to give some background information and to explain the various changes of name.

There were some very early hospitals in the city: St John's dating from the twelfth century, St Catherine's which was founded in 1552, and Bellot's Hospital founded in 1609. They provided some medical and nursing care but were essentially almshouses for a few elderly and impoverished people. The first hospital built in Bath specifically for medical treatment was the General Hospital, founded in 1742. As far as patients in Bath were concerned, however, this was a misleading title because residents of the city were not admitted there during its first hundred years, earning it the name The Hospital for the Reception of Strangers.[1] It is now known as the Royal National Hospital for Rheumatic Diseases, and has also been called the Mineral Water Hospital.

In Bath in the eighteenth century, for residents who had money, there were numerous doctors offering treatment at home where servants could do the nursing. Most of the elegant visitors who came to Bath could afford lodgings in the larger houses, and local doctors visited them there to give advice on how much of the mineral water to drink or how often to use the baths. But poorer people also came to Bath from other parts of the country, hoping for a cure they could not afford, and it was reported that 'the constant influx of the maimed, the halt and the blind, who pestered the inhabitants and visitors, made the city a Mecca for beggars.'[2] This must have been an embarrassment for fashionable Georgian Bath and the Mineral Water Hospital was built to contain these sick vagrants. The poor people of Bath, equally in need of treatment, were not admitted because it was presumed they already had some form of accommodation.

Something had to be done for the local people, and five years after the opening of that hospital for strangers an appeal was made for the funding of a charity named The Pauper Scheme. Several books on the history of Bath have given different addresses for the original location of the charity. Some state that it started in a rented house on Lower Borough Walls, some quote Wood Street, and another insisted that it started in 17 Kingsmead Street. It is possible that it could have been housed in any or all of these places at various times, because those early small charities were usually in rented premises and frequently moved from one address to another. So it is difficult to determine the original site, but all sources agree that the charity was founded in 1747.

The earliest Bath Guides only state that it dispensed free medicines to poor residents within the city boundaries and in the villages of Walcot and Widcombe, offering treatment to patients in their homes. It seems that no beds were provided and patients needing accommodation or special nursing were boarded out with local responsible people, as shown in a broadsheet of 1760.[3] For example:

Elizabeth Stevens was paid for two weeks nursing, diet and lodgings for John Coombs, a pauper with contusion on both thighs - one guinea.

£3 12s 11d paid for nursing and housing William Wall for seven weeks while he had a broken leg.

John Reeves was paid £4 3s 0d for ten weeks mainte- nance of John Blatchley, a pauper with a fractured leg.

A few years later in 1766 there was the first mention of inpatient treatment when the charity was renamed "The Pau- per Scheme Enlarged". Surgical treatment was offered and beds were to be provided, 'a number not exceeding four',[4] al- though it is not said how many patients would occupy the beds. In the Bristol Royal Infirmary, patients were two to a bed for many years,[5] so it is more than possible that there were two patients to each frame in Bath's small charity.

By 1792 larger premises were needed. The Pauper Scheme moved to a house on the Lower Borough Walls, formerly the Alfred Hotel, which gave space for a resident apothecary and a matron. There was a room to be used as a dispensary, an- other for outpatients, and six beds for inpatients. At this new location the charity was renamed The City Infirmary and Dispensary. By that time it no longer offered surgical treat- ment because another hospital had opened which, according to the report of the Annual General Meeting, 'was more es- pecially calculated to afford assistance in surgical cases'.

This was the Casualty Hospital which was founded in Kingsmead Street in 1788. Its main function was the treat- ment of accidents, many of them among labourers working on houses in the city during the big building boom of that time, and it had an average of eight beds. 38 Kingsmead Street is still there, now functioning as a fish and chip shop.

By 1820 it was acknowledged that neither the Casualty Hospital nor the Infirmary were in premises large enough to provide the services necessary for Bath's rapidly growing population,[6] and that the solution would be a merger of the two institutions in a new building. Appeals were made to the public for funds and negotiations were begun for a suitable site. Local newspapers printed letters which indicated that there were disagreements about the viability of the merger and about the choice of site. Eventually land next to the old Infirmary was chosen and Bath United Hospital opened in June 1826 in the building which, a hundred years later, was bought by Bath Technical College. St Catherine's almshouse had been on part of the chosen site, in what was described as 'an old and mean building'. It was later demolished and re-placed by new premises further along Bilbury Lane. The Old Bath and Sun Fire Office had used another part of the land. This was removed, but the shed that had previously housed the fire engine apparently remained for some time because, in 1828, when the hospital was asked to admit sick soldiers from the 21st Fusiliers, it was decided that 'the small build-ing, late the Engine Shed' would be suitable accommodation for them. The new building was joined to the old infirmary by a corridor known as the Long Room, which was used as a li-brary for medical books and as a museum for pathology specimens. The drawing room of the old house later became a surgical ward and the rest of the ancient infirmary building was in use for the next forty years.

The original plans for the hospital building mentioned 100 beds, but it was a long time before that number was reached and an average of 70 patients was maintained for many years. A mineral water bath for the use of patients was also part of the original planning and letters were sent to the Mayor suggesting that a supply could be diverted to the hospital from the 'superabundance flowing from the neighbouring baths', but it seems that this did not happen. Arrangements were made instead for patients to be treated at the city's baths, in a special large tub that was maintained and repaired at the hospital's expense.

When the Poor Law Amendment Act was introduced in 1834, a survey of Bath district at that time concluded that more medical services were needed over a larger area. Within the city boundaries the United Hospital dispensed medicines and the Apothecary gave treatment to impoverished people in their homes, but more facilities were necessary for patients living further from the centre of town. So three dispensaries were started, the Southern Dispensary to cover the area around Lyncombe and Widcombe, the Eastern Dispensary for north and east Walcot, and the Western Dispensary for the region north of the river to New Bridge. They all provided medicine and dealt with minor cases, including the treatment of children, who were not admitted to the United Hospital at that time. More serious medical and surgical cases from all districts were treated at Bath United Hospital and its services were gradually expanded until it covered a hundred parishes in a region with a twenty mile radius around the city.

2

Early Administration

The hospital was ruled by a committee of local worthies, many of them retired naval or military officers. They met weekly on Mondays and never a week was missed, with the only exception that when Christmas Day was on a Monday the Committee met on Boxing Day. The minutes of those meetings, from 1827 onwards, are in the Record Office at the Guildhall in Bath. They contain very few references to individual patients or their ailments, but statistics on the various conditions treated were printed in the volumes of annual reports, many of them available at Bath Central Library.

Those Monday meetings covered all aspects of administration from finance to food, from railways to ringworm, and from the entries in the minutes it is possible to learn about the sights, the sounds and even the smells of the building. Because the hospital was initially surrounded by an assortment of dilapidated homes, there was an early complaint about 'the nuisance to the hospital from the open privies of the adjoining houses'. Later there was mention of 'obnoxious aromas from the nearby rag and bone yard and offensive odours from a pig tub'.

Noise from horse drawn traffic was another problem, so the cobblestones around the hospital were covered with wooden paving to try to minimise it. A few years later attempts were made to have tramlines diverted. There were also frequent complaints about the noise from numerous brass bands on Saturday afternoons and of 'drunken revellers' at night. In the 1830s there were complaints about medical students who were 'playing musical instruments and making noise injurious to the patients'. This was not their only sin. One of them 'wantonly set fire to some turpentine' and all were accused of insubordination and negligence. There was one gruesome incident when a student was practising dissection on a dog which ran into the street during attempts to cut off its head, resulting in complaints from the public.

Equally gruesome was the disclosure that parts of bodies used by the students for dissection were being buried in the back garden of the hospital and, in the minutes of the following Monday, there was a decision that the area should be immediately covered with paving. This could prove interesting for any future archaeologists who might explore the precincts of the old building. Several years ago on local radio it was said that workmen digging near the foundations of the Bristol Royal Infirmary had discovered a great many old bones which apparently were not old enough to have been part of a plague pit and could not be explained, so maybe Bath United Hospital was not the only one where efforts were made to cut the time and cost involved in arranging more suitable burials.

These troubles were minor inconveniences compared with those of 1865 when an extension to the hospital was being built and funds were too low to cover costs. The workmen went on strike for unpaid wages and scaffolding was liable to be seized. The architect was offered only a small part of his fee and threatened to sue, so the minutes were full of legal letters plus many suggestions for cutting costs. The situation was saved by the people of Bath who organised an enormous bazaar which raised £1884 (the present day equivalent would be approximately £76,000) so the building

15

was finally completed. Because the extension was dedicated to Prince Albert who had recently died, in May 1868 Queen Victoria gave permission for the title Royal United Hospital to be used and, in photographs taken in the early 1900s, the dedication to 'Albert The Good' can be seen painted in large white lettering on the extended building.

While the foundations for the extension were being excavated, Roman remains were discovered. They were described as 'an elaborate suite of Roman Baths'[7] but only a tessellated pavement was kept in situ. From a sketch made when it was discovered, and from the colouring described, it must have been an attractive example of a Roman floor. Some of Bath's history books state that it was moved from the hospital to the newly opened Roman Baths Museum in 1897 but, though there were plans for this at the time, it did not arrive at the museum. Extracts from the minute books show efforts made to preserve the floor, but the hospital could not provide the necessary funds (see Appendix B). It seems that the pavement deteriorated to such an extent that it did not justify inclusion in the Museum, so whatever remained must be somewhere under the building which later became Bath Technical College.

It seems surprising that railways needed discussion by the Committee, but an entry in 1837 recorded that application had been made to the Great Western Railway for an increased annual sum. This was to cover treatment for the many casualties among labourers employed in the construction of Brunel's line from London to Bristol. The subscription was raised to five guineas at that time, but in later minute books there were several entries showing that amounts paid by the GWR could not cover treatment for the large number of patients involved. Reminders were constantly sent for overdue subscriptions but it was not until 1893 that the hospital publicly expressed indignation. Several casualties had received treatment after a derailment in the Box Tunnel, but only £20 was donated by the GWR. At the Annual General Meeting of the hospital, which was reported in local papers, the Chairman made some very derisory remarks about the paltry amounts received from the company.

In 1877 the hospital was involved in what was known as the Widcombe Bridge Disaster. A train arrived at the station from Salisbury and passengers were surging across the river to an agricultural show when the bridge collapsed. Nine people died and sixty were injured, forty-five of whom were admitted to the hospital. It was proudly recorded that they were treated (presumably sewn, splinted and bandaged) and were all in bed within one hour and twenty minutes – an early example of efficient disaster management! For its prompt actions the hospital received public praise, and donations totalling £400 were received from various individuals and societies.

3
Nursing

In the minute books the first reference to nursing was in 1833 when a night nurse was dismissed for stealing bread from a patient. During her hours of duty she would have received some sort of meal, but at that time nurses were not resident in the hospital and she may have been trying to take food home to a family living at starvation level. Such a desperate need was probably due to her very low salary of only £8 a year – an indication of the poor opinion in which nurses were held at that time. In the 1840s a surgeon at St Thomas' Hospital in London classed all nurses as 'drunken, ignorant and promiscuous', and in 1888 Sir James Paget, recalling the type of nurse he knew when he started his medical training, said:

> 'There were some excellent nurses, especially in the medical wards where everything was more gentle and orderly than on the surgical side where they could not have kept a chart or taken a temperature'.[8]

He remembered one surgical sister who was 'rough tongued and scolding' but was observant, helpful... and only sometimes tipsy.

An entry in the early RUH minute books records that one nurse was dismissed after reporting for duty in what was described as 'an advanced state of intoxication'. There was another who was accused of neglect on night duty when a patient with heart disease fell through the sacking base of his bed onto the floor. Other patients tried to mend the bed and put him back, but he fell through again. It was later reported that 'all this time the nurse was in the ward and dozing by the fire'. The Committee then decided that something must be done to improve the standard of nursing, but reform was slow and supervision must have been lax. One nurse was guilty of leaving the patients in her ward to dispense all the medicines to each other as they thought fit. A few years later, another was rebuked for injecting a patient with carbolic acid 'when she had no orders to do so'.

Florence Nightingale's campaign improved the standard of nursing when she insisted that an entirely new type of 'Lady Nurse' was needed, fully trained and always personally clean and neat.[9] Her ideas for reform reached Bath in the 1860s when the RUH founded the Training Institute, an apprenticeship system for nurses' education, during which time they must learn:

> To cook gruel, egg flip and puddings.
> The best method of friction to the body and the extremities.
> The application of leeches externally and internally.

In 1862 there was a ruling that nurses must not wear crinolines in the wards, a sensible ban at a time when fashion extremes had resulted in hoops of enormous size and when space between beds was limited. Material was provided for indoor uniforms but trainees supplied their own uniform cloaks and bonnets. Recruits to the Training Institute were between the ages of 20 and 25 and, because they received no pay for the first year, they tended to come from a middle class background where contribution to family income was not essential. It was stressed that they must also be 'in good health, of moral character and average height'. Practical training was given in the wards for three years and the students were then available for hospital posts or could be sent out to care for private patients, for which service the RUH charged fees up to two guineas a week. In this way the hospital not only gained funds but also had a reserve of partly or fully trained help as an addition to the existing nursing staff.

These trainees were apparently living at home because it was not until 1890 that a residential nurse training school was opened in Hot Bath Street. Lectures were organised by the matron or doctors and there were examinations at the end of each course with awards of gold or silver medals. A press photograph of the period shows two award winners wearing elaborate caps with large bows under the chin. At times the examination results were disappointing as, for example, in 1898 when it was said that the trainees had 'little knowledge of invalid feeding and did not know how to make a charcoal poultice'.

Not all RUH nurses were trained at the Institute. Those who could not afford to live without that first year's salary entered the hospital as probationers, and for them life was hard. They spent long hours scrubbing floors and, with no official pension scheme, they must have dreaded increasing age or illness. One nurse was dismissed 'for having a long-concealed ulcerated leg' and another was sent to the workhouse when she was unfit for duty. However, in 1852, a charity named The Sutcliffe Memorial Fund was formed to give a yearly pension to retired nurses. In one case this meant an allowance of two shillings and sixpence a week in recognition of twenty-two years work in the hospital. Another nurse, after eleven years service, had been given a single gratuity of £3. She was later reported as being in financial trouble, so a further £2 was given to cover rent arrears.

Before 1880, nurses who lived in the hospital had to apply for a special permit to leave the building, and for night nurses the system was severely regulated. Night nurses were on duty from 10pm to 10am and they were then allowed 'two hours for exercise'. Dinner was at 12.30pm, after which they must assist with patients' lunches. They were finally released from duty at 2pm, presumably to sleep in their dormitory, which had five beds in a space 15 feet by 20 feet. For day nursing, the 1861 revision introduced three new categories with Head Nurses earning £21 a year (£860 at present day value), Ordinary Nurses earning £16 and Scrubbers earning £10 annually. For this they worked twelve hours a day and were only allowed out of the hospital on alternate Sundays from 6pm to 9pm to attend church services. Only after the First World War was consideration given for a reduction to nine hours a day in a six day week. It was a general rule that no married nurses were employed in hospitals and, although some married voluntary nurses from the Red Cross and St John Ambulance served in the First World War, for regular nursing staff the ban remained for many years afterwards.

General living conditions for RUH nurses improved after 1890, probably because the hospital had been left with only one qualified nurse on the staff. Six had resigned the previous year after complaining about low wages, about cramped cubicles in the dormitories and about poor sanitary arrangements. So six houses in Hot Bath Street were rented from the Corporation giving space for Matron and nurses to have separate bedrooms over the new outpatients department on the ground floor. Holiday leave (unpaid) was granted for two weeks a year and salaries were raised from £30 to £40 per annum. In an annual report of this period the Mayor stated that Bath trained nurses were highly regarded in London. This high standard must have resulted in a certain amount of poaching of nurses because it was necessary to impose a rule that any nurse who left shortly after being trained by the RUH must not take nursing work, either privately or in an institution, within a radius of six miles from Bath. Failure to observe the rule would incur a £20 fine, the equivalent of six months salary.

Living conditions for nurses in all hospitals may have improved during the century, but an article in Frazer's Magazine in 1891 warned that there were hazards in the profession:

> 'Nurses are liable to premature decline and rheumatic nervous suffering in old age. Attending patients of the opposite sex could prove a severe test and would only be overcome by steady and conscientious practice'

Perhaps this is why, a few years later when voluntary nurses (VADs) were being trained before World War One, they were told that their ministrations to soldiers would be restricted to hands and feet only. However, the desperate need for nurses after war was declared soon caused a change in the rule.

There were still long working hours for trainee nurses at the RUH. Lectures and study were fitted into free time, and on night duty they were expected to mend linen, patch sheets and make pillow cases from the old linen sent in by the public. They sewed shrouds in stiff calico and there were always bandages to be washed, ironed, and rolled on special machines.

On Monday mornings the Sister of each ward read out the hospital bye-laws for the benefit of the patients, and evening prayers were taken in every ward by a Sister or Staff Nurse. In the RUH minutes there is no record of junior nurses having to kneel at Sister's feet during these prayers, as happened at other hospitals, but certain rules about nursing status were clearly recorded. No lesser nurse was allowed to sit down in the ward without the consent of Sister. No probationer was permitted to address a Sister directly, and questions during lectures were never allowed. In 1911 the Sisters informed the Committee that they 'wished to have their meals apart from nurses of lower rank', so it was agreed that a special table would be set aside for them, a system which existed in most hospitals for many years.

The First World War accentuated the need for trained nurses, and by the 1930s when the RUH moved from the city to Combe Park the standard of nursing was high. It was considered that the move to higher ground would improve the health of staff because it was said that 'hospital sore throat', which had previously troubled the nurses, was 'practically unknown on the Combe Park site'.

Matrons

In 1829, three years after the founding of the United Hospital, it was reported that the matron was not as efficient as she had been. She must previously have been employed either in the Casualty Hospital or the old Infirmary because it was said that she had served a total of twenty-six years. She was eighty years old and it was time for her to go. There may have been some doubts too about her literacy, because the Committee, when considering her replacement, agreed that it would be an improvement if future nursing staff could read and write.

Later, matrons were held in higher regard and compared with the other nursing staff their living conditions were amazingly different. Matrons had an annual salary of £50 at a time when nurses were receiving only £15. No official paid leave was granted to ordinary nurses until 1922, but Mrs Johnstone, successor to the elderly matron, managed to have at least two weeks leave in most years from 1838 onwards. She had her own newly furnished parlour, plus bedchamber, and was allowed to have her niece sharing them with her for six years.

When Mrs Johnstone resigned, her replacement, Mrs Thornthwaite, was equally indulged. She also had frequent leave, was allowed to have her daughter lodging with her for several years, and received many £10 gratuities in addition to her salary. The Apothecary was instructed to supply her with 'small quantities of wine and brandy from time to time plus an unlimited supply of beer', but the alcohol may not have been for her sole use because the resident doctors ate their meals in Matron's parlour for many years. She must have been greatly valued by the management board because, on two occasions when she was ill, the hospital granted £5 for a coach to enable her to take 'daily rides out of town for the benefit of her health' – a very different approach from the dismissal of the nurse who tried to conceal her ulcerated legs. A later matron put in a request for a personal maid, but although she suggested that such a person could occasionally help with sewing for the hospital, it is not surprising that this request was refused.

Advertisements for replacement matrons were always placed in Bath and Bristol papers plus the British Medical Journal and the London Times. Nursing experience may not have been of primary importance; a knowledge of house-keeping in a large establishment was perhaps more appropriate, because a list of Matron's duties included the care of all household goods and furniture. She kept all keys and was responsible for security. She weighed and measured all provisions delivered to the hospital, keeping records of various diets and of the many gifts of food or linen sent in by the public. She was responsible for all domestic staff, checked every room in the hospital daily and visited each ward morning and evening. In later years the appointment of the House Steward or Hospital Secretary relieved matrons from most of their responsibility for provisions and domestic duties, enabling them to give more time to patients and to the supervision of nursing staff.

Not all matrons were of a high standard. In 1899 one was asked to resign after an accusation that she had acquired a bottle of whisky sent in for a patient and that she had verbally abused two nurses 'in a most unwomanly way'.

However, by the 1930s Miss Nightingale's hopes for 'Lady Nurses' from middle class families had obviously materialised. When Miss Vian was appointed matron to the RUH, all the local newspapers stressed that she was the sister of Rear Admiral Vian, who had served in the First World War. At this time the duties of the matron included recruitment and responsibility, not only for nursing staff, but also for physiotherapists and radiographers. Miss Vian was matron from 1930 to 1938, and in 1932 she was responsible for organising the move from the city to the new buildings at Combe Park. There her duties expanded when she acted also as Advisory Matron to the Orthopaedic and Forbes Fraser hospitals, which had been built on the site six years earlier.

4

Patients

Bath's elegant buildings may give the impression that for residents in the Georgian period the city was a place of wealth and comfort. But there was much real poverty, particularly in the houses near the river in the southern parts of the town. A broadsheet printed in 1771 said that the Pauper Charity had given medical aid to a large number of patients, 'most of them in the greatest distress',[10] and when the services of the hospital later expanded to cover rural areas, agricultural workers were among the poorest of patients. In the middle of the nineteenth century most farm labourers in Somerset and Wiltshire were employed only for short seasonal periods, earning less than ten shillings a week. Although some landowners did provide full employment and adequate housing for their workers, many cottages were damp and insanitary. Even worse were the frequent cases where large families were living in nothing more than draughty sheds built against existing walls.[11]

The original rules for the Pauper Charity stressed that its services were 'only for the benefit of the poor and no persons in good circumstance should apply'. There was no admittance for cases of psychiatric disorder, nor for 'any persons from a common brothel' – they were sent to the workhouse. Rules covering the tickets necessary for admission varied over the years, but at first they were essential for both inpatient or outpatient treatment. To get one, the patient, or a relative, would apply either to the vicarage or to a wealthy local subscriber. It then had to be taken to the Parish Overseer for a signature to confirm that the patient was not receiving financial help locally.

Transport to the hospital must have been difficult for patients in the days before the introduction of public services. In the minute books of 1864 there is a letter from the mayor of Bath complaining about 'the evil of conveying poor persons with infectious diseases to the Bath United Hospital in ordinary flys or chairs', to which the hospital sharply replied that there was 'the same risk to carriages when rich infected patients were carried'. It added that dedicated hospital transport was not advisable because 'the terror excited by the use of a special carriage might provoke fatal results'. Dr Charles Marsh, a general practitioner in Bath from 1906 said that:

> An ambulance service as we know it now simply did not exist. There was an ambulance nominally, but it was horse-drawn and so seldom used that the driver was full-time on other work. He had to be recalled from that work, get the horse out, and in due time attend, but it meant hours of delay.[12]

As late as 1918, an entry in the minutes stated that the hospital could not be responsible for transporting patients.

All outpatients were instructed to report to the department at 10.30am to wait on rows of long wooden forms, and there were frequent letters in the press complaining about delays. Conditions probably improved in 1908 when the hospital expanded into several houses in Hot Bath Street giving space for a larger outpatient department, and in January 1918 an entry in the minutes noted that the waiting room had been 'warmed for the first time'.

Admission as an inpatient must have been terrifying in

27

the days before anaesthesia. But after the pain and discomfort had lessened, for those patients who normally endured appalling living conditions, the hospital must have seemed a warm and comfortable place. Oil lamps were the main form of lighting, plus lanthorns or candles, and there were fires in every ward, protected by high semi-circular fire guards, around which clothes were often aired. There were stone hot water bottles in winter and, for some chronic patients, there were water beds, which may seem to be a recent invention but were first referred to in the minutes for October 1836. In the early days beds were merely iron frames with sacking fixed across the base; the mattresses were filled with straw or flock (later replaced by 'curled hair or mill puff') and local newspapers carried constant appeals for old linen to make sheets and pillowcases.

Many patients arrived in rags which were burnt and replaced. Dressing gowns were lined in red flannel, the material which was considered to give maximum warmth, and several dozen nightcaps were ordered at intervals. There were orders for slippers to be made by the children of Bath's Ragged School. A charity known as the Flannel Society provided flannel waistcoats for both sexes, with red flannel petticoats for females, and various other items of clothing for use in hospital and also after discharge.

Each May and October the hospital minute books listed tenders from various local firms giving prices of fuel, laundry or food, and for patients who had previously existed at starvation level, a few weeks in hospital must have meant an increase in weight. According to diet lists for the 1800s, patients received daily servings of four ounces of beef or mutton, inevitably followed by milk puddings. During the Irish famine 'rice with cabbage' was the substitute for rare and costly potatoes. When funds were low the management board discussed cheaper cuts of meat for beef tea and solemnly considered the need to omit raisins from bread and butter puddings. But there was always extra food for celebrations such as Queen Victoria's Jubilee, or for the relief of Mafeking when there was 'A Special Tea and Smoking Concert in one of the wards'. Each Christmas, the matron received extra money for puddings and cakes, pork for the patients and goose or turkey for the doctors.

A few days before Christmas 1871 the Bath Chronicle described one visiting day:

> At the entrance a crowd generally exceeding 100,
> sometimes nearly 200, waited for the clock to strike
> three for visits to patients where there is scrupulous
> cleanliness, glowing fires, pictures and Christmas
> decorations.

The minute books give names of patients only when extended time was needed for treatment, but the Surgical In-patients Book for the period 1891-1898 gives brief details of one patient who spent ten days over Christmas receiving treatment for chilblains. This was Charlie Bush, a farm labourer aged thirteen, and the fact that he needed surgery as an inpatient indicates that the swellings had become open sores that needed stitches. To get to such a state, he must have been very cold and probably undernourished for a very long time and was surely one patient who benefited, though briefly, from the warmth, from the clothing and from extra food that Christmas.

For most of the nineteenth century small beer was drunk instead of the unsafe water, and wines and spirits were often part of medical treatment, with a ticket attached to each patient's bed noting the alcohol prescribed. In 1856 there were complaints that:

> The Marsala wine provided for the patients is inferior and expensive at twenty eight shillings for a dozen bottles while the Workhouse has good Sherry provided at fourteen shillings a gallon.

So four gallons of the sherry were ordered. Thirteen years later, when the hospital was in deep financial trouble, there were overall economies but the order list for alcohol that year still included 'red Spanish wine, pale sherry, golden sherry, brandy, rum and beer'.

The RUH was a Church of England concern, only recruiting staff of that religion, and at times there was conflict when Catholic priests or non-conformist ministers were refused entry to the hospital for visits to parishioners. There was a chapel where convalescent patients were expected to attend all services and, as in all charities in Victorian times, there was much emphasis on prayer and moral values. A booklet printed for patients at one hospital gave the sombre warning that: 'As sickness is the usual forerunner of death it should therefore lend you seriously to consider and reflect on your behaviour in life', and books donated by the public to the patients' library at the RUH stressed the same theme. One had the title 'The Pious Christian's Daily Preparation for Death and Eternity', and others had similarly gloomy sentiments.

One ward at the hospital was reserved for privileged patients. Frequently when servants were ill they were just dismissed from the houses where they worked, but some employers subscribed to the RUH and also paid ten or twelve shillings a week for their workers to be admitted to The Servants Ward. Those who were abandoned by their employers were accepted in the common wards or were sent to the workhouse. Mr Jolly (of Milsom Street) was prepared to pay that extra sum when one of his servants developed smallpox in 1857, but fever cases were not admitted to the hospital so he rented rooms at 15 St James Place and, because he was a good benefactor, RUH doctors visited the patient there.

The food and warmth in the hospital may have provided a temporary respite from extreme hardship, but for some people it was too late and the death rate was high, particularly in the winter months. In 1895 most of England was covered in several feet of snow for many weeks and the hospital minutes record that out of 128 patients, 30 died in one week. Before 1900 the average inpatient stay was from 33 to 49 days, and during their stay patients were instructed to 'conduct themselves in a decent and orderly manner' with strict obedience to rules. There is no mention in RUH records of domestic duties for male convalescent patients, but the women were expected to assist with cleaning, laundry or sewing. When there was a shortage of nurses, patients under treatment filled the vacancies.

When in 1887 there were complaints about patients being turned out of their beds before 5am, the matron said that this was necessary for good nursing management; over forty years later patients were still being roused at 5am for washing. Visiting times were restricted to one hour, from 3pm to 4pm, on two days a week, but in 1896 the rules were amended to allow very ill patients to have daily short visits from close relatives. There was a strict rule that convalescent patients must stand by their beds when the matron or a doctor entered the ward and at those times talking between patients was strictly forbidden.

Other rules were printed regularly in the annual reports. They threatened confiscation of any 'liquids or eatables' brought to the hospital by patients or visitors and also warned that practising 'any species of gambling' would mean instant dismissal. One rule was not included in the annual printed list, but in June 1889 the Committee obviously felt it necessary to record an entry in the minute book to ensure that 'For the future no dancing to be allowed in the wards'.

When patients were discharged they were given a letter for their local parson, a printed form of thanksgiving for recovery and for the excellent services rendered by the RUH. This was to be read out by the parson at the next Sunday service while the patient stood in front of the congregation in a small ceremony to enhance the reputation of the hospital and encourage the onlookers to increase their donations.

5

Children

In the earliest records of the hospital there was no reference to children because they were not admitted for treatment, and this applied at most general hospitals in England at that time. It was considered preferable for children to be treated in their homes because there was risk that they would carry their juvenile diseases to hospital wards. Also, before the days of diagnostic tools such as stethoscopes and thermometers, children were considered difficult patients because they could not easily describe their pain or discomfort.[13] In later RUH records there were occasional references to child patients. For example, in 1844 an infant was admitted for operation on a club foot, and his mother was also admitted to the ward, possibly because the child was breast fed. One or two children, generally over the age of six, were later admitted to beds in adult wards, and eventually a small room was set aside for child care. In 1885, girls at Bath High School were sewing clothes for young patients and three years later the children of St Mary's Church in Bathwick raised sufficient money to buy three cots for that room.

A special children's ward containing twenty cots was built over the Albert Wing in 1891, and donors often specified that money was to be used only for the children. Among toys received as gifts there was a miniature grocer's shop, a doll's house and a rocking horse, and, in 1906, 'a handsome mechanical bird in a cage'. The Mayor of Bath was obviously aware that the public placed great value in this ward, and in a desperate appeal for funds in 1902 he included a little blackmail. He said that there might be need to close parts of the hospital, starting with the children's ward, and this would inevitably result in 'much suffering for those dear sick little ones'.

By this time the hospital was also taking a more active part in the treatment of schoolchildren as outpatients, particularly for ringworm and for removal of tonsils. For that operation conditions seem to have been less than ideal because the waiting room was also the recovery room. In a complaint from school authorities it was said that postoperative cases returned to that room 'semi conscious, their mouths stained with blood, to be handed to their mothers who attempted to mop up the blood from their throats'. This was having such an adverse effect that those children who had experienced hospital treatment dreaded even routine medical inspections carried out at schools.

6
Doctors

No history of a hospital would be complete without reference to its doctors, but much has already been written by other authors about the more prominent of Bath's physicians and surgeons, so only a few of those who attended the hospital are mentioned here.

Before the introduction of the National Health Service, consultants gained their income from their private patients and gave their services free to institutions like the RUH. They were elected as honorary medical staff by those members of the public who donated regularly to the hospital, and in the earlier days up to 1000 ballot papers were issued for each new appointment, with between 400 and 600 votes registered. Appointment to an honorary post in a charity hospital brought with it a prestige that could lead to an increase in private practice, so competition was keen. It was not unusual for candidates to do a certain amount of canvassing, encouraging friends and relatives to become subscribers in order to register votes. Although the election system was amended over the years, applicants for hospital appointment must still have been trying to use influence in 1905 because an entry in the minutes made it clear that those found canvassing would be disqualified. These honorary doctors also attended patients at other institutions in Bath such as the Mineral Water Hospital, the Eye Hospital, and the Puerperal Charity, which cared for impoverished women in pregnancy.

Early doctors

Caleb Hillier Parry came to Bath in 1779 and was the most outstanding of the honorary physicians who attended patients at the Pauper Charity. He died in 1822 and was buried in Bath Abbey where his memorial, written in Latin, refers to his studies in many subjects. His detailed notes contributed a great deal to the understanding of thyroid disease and its effect on the heart, and he gave dissertations on rabies and tetanus. But his research was not confined to medicine.

On his farm at Summerhill on the slopes of Lansdown he experimented in the breeding of sheep to produce a higher standard of wool,[14] a subject financially important in England at that time, and his papers were published in the Transactions of the Board of Agriculture.[15] He studied minerals and fossils and exchanged information with many well-known scientists: with William Herschel the astronomer, with Joseph Priestley who discovered oxygen, and with his lifelong friend Edward Jenner whose research into cowpox helped to eradicate the spread of smallpox. There is some indication about the character of the man, and of his philosophical attitude to research, from his introduction to a discussion on angina:

> In reality it is of little importance who is the discoverer of truths, however valuable. For mankind it suffices that the truth is actually known and the good obtained.[16]

Parry gathered a unique collection of 550 early medical books, the earliest of which was a treatise on surgery produced in Venice in 1498. He also had many other rare editions covering the next three centuries.[17] After his death his son, Dr Charles Parry, sold Summerhill House and offered the books to the RUH on condition that the collection would be cared for and would never be sold. For many years attempts were made to ensure that these books were properly maintained in the Board Room at the hospital, but eventually the collection became a liability. Although it was described in the press in 1932 as 'the world famous library of Dr Parry', lack of funds for the new building at Combe Park meant that no provision could be made for library space and the books were sent to the Medical School Library at Bristol University. There they are known as The Parry Collection, despite the fact that 220 of the original books came from the library of John Smith Soden, one of Parry's contemporaries.

John Smith Soden had a son John Soden, also a surgeon at the United Hospital at the same time as his father – all very confusing for historians when some of the records omit 'Smith' from items on John Senior – and there were several other dynasties among Bath's early doctors.

James Norman, another contemporary of Caleb Parry, was one of the founders of the Casualty Hospital in Kingsmead Street, but he resigned after thirty years because he strongly objected to the proposed site for the union of that hospital with the Infirmary.

He retained an interest in the Puerperal or Childbed Charity and, in a letter to the press marking his disapproval he advised 'those Pregnant Women who seek relief to apply in future at his house, No.24 New King Street any Monday at 11 o'clock and not at the Casualty Hospital as heretofore.' In 1816, four years before James Norman protested about the union, his son George Norman had been appointed as surgeon to the Casualty Hospital and later worked for the new United Hospital until 1856.

There were three generations of physicians named Falconer. William Falconer, who came from Chester to Bath in 1770, was a prolific writer on the healing powers of Bath waters and on other medical subjects. He wrote on the effects of copper poisoning, on the health of farm workers, on fevers and 'the influence of passions upon disorders of the body'. His son Thomas also qualified as a doctor but seems to have had little association with the United Hospital apart from donations to the charity.

William's grandson Randle Wilbraham Falconer was a well-known personage in Bath. He was associated with the hospital for thirty-one years, was President for a time, and was also Mayor of Bath. Like his grandfather he wrote many articles on the properties of Bath waters. He wrote on gout and rheumatism and gave lectures on health and how to preserve it, but he concentrated even more on hospital management. Family connections and civic status may have helped, but Randle Falconer certainly had a greater influence on the daily administration of the RUH than any other doctor of that time. He was mentioned frequently in the minute books in 1864 when he visited several hospitals in Somerset and Wiltshire to record details of financial management, to compare salaries or duties of nursing staff and to assess the merits of various types of lift used in different institutions.

In comparison with that of Randle Falconer the name of Edward Barlow was rarely mentioned in the minutes despite the fact that he diagnosed the first cases of cholera when the epidemic reached Bath in 1832,[18] and was an active member of Bath's Provincial and Medical Society where local doctors discussed diseases and treatments. But it is possible to gain an impression of him through the eyes of one of his pauper patients, Eliza Day.[19] Eliza, at seven years old in 1826, was apprenticed to a farmer in Devon. She was starved and beaten by her employer so, at the end of her fourteen-year apprenticeship, she walked from Devon to Bath where she was admitted to the United Hospital for six weeks. There she appreciated the kindness and the treatment given by Dr Barlow, who was apparently so popular with his patients that they composed a verse about him:

Dr Barlow he comes in
And looks as noble as a king
He smells as sweet as any rose
He views his patients and out he goes.

To destitute patients the early honorary doctors must have seemed impressive and almost regal. When the Pauper Scheme started the doctors would have worn wigs and court dress consisting of an elegant frock coat worn with breeches, silk or wool stockings and buckled shoes. By the 1840s, when the verse about Dr Barlow was in circulation, clothes were simpler. According to portraits of that time, he would have been wearing a fine linen shirt with full sleeves, and a silk or linen cravat at the neck, with a frock coat that may have been of velvet worn open to show a patterned waistcoat with gold watch and chain.

It is possible that he had a scent of roses because men used lavender or rosewater liberally at that time. As a physician his personal smell may have been sweeter than that of some surgeons, who often kept old coats to be used in the operating theatre. After some months or even years of autopsies and operations, these coats could be stiff with blood or other secretions.

The last line of the rhyme may have been a reference to the brevity of Dr Barlow's visits. In the Bristol Royal Infirmary at that period it was recorded that only one and a half minutes was the time honorary staff allotted to each patient,[20] and this probably applied in most charity hospitals.

When Eliza was discharged from hospital the matron gave her clothing which would have come from the Flannel Waistcoat Society, a charity founded by Edward Barlow in

1824 to provide patients with warm garments for use in hospital and also after discharge. This type of practical care was mentioned in Barlow's obituary in the Bath Herald of 1844 which stressed his 'humane consideration for his patients, his deep and tender sympathy with every individual, their suffering and their wants'.

With the exception of Randle Wilbraham Falconer, visiting consultants had little direct influence on hospital administration. They were allowed one vote in ballots, but in the earlier period of the hospital they were not admitted to Management Committee meetings. They could only exert influence by writing letters with suggestions – or more often complaints – about administration. When the hospital was in deep financial trouble in 1868 the Committee decided to dispense with the post of matron and, without consulting the medical staff, appointed instead a senior nurse at a lower salary. This resulted in a letter from the honorary doctors saying that 'understanding between Management and Staff was thus even more remote than hitherto'.

Later there were threatened resignations because the Committee was appointing unqualified medical staff and 'the views and suggestions of the physicians were continuously disregarded'.

In the 1880s the doctors formed a Medical Board whose president could liase with the Committee. Eight years later, honorary medical staff were admitted as members of the Committee with special responsibility for checking that applicants for junior posts had the necessary medical qualifications. But the difficult relationship between medical and administrative staff was not completely overcome.

Resident Medical Staff

Long before the founding of the Pauper Scheme there were apothecaries who, in addition to selling medicines from small shops, treated patients in their homes. The five-year apprenticeship necessary for them to be accepted as members of the Society of Apothecaries gave them good medical experience and they can probably be regarded as the earliest family practitioners.

When the Pauper Charity expanded to larger premises in 1792 there was living accommodation for an apothecary, who was the first resident medical member of staff. He was responsible for home visits to outpatients within the city boundaries and he also dealt with night emergencies at the hospital, both medical and surgical. In 1849 he was given the title of House Apothecary and Physician's Assistant. His other duties included the supervision of nurses ('with particular attention to instances of misconduct') and ensuring there was adequate ventilation throughout the hospital. The earliest minute books record an average of eighteen home visits daily, but these fluctuated during various epidemics. In the hospital yearbook for 1858 the House Apothecary, Mr Fowler, received acclaim for his work during an outbreak of smallpox when he coped with 116 inpatients and 325 outpatients. His salary was £100 a year, in addition to his keep, and eight years later the longer title was changed to that of Resident Medical Officer.

A house surgeon was the second resident member appointed to the Pauper Charity, but for many years this was not a salaried post. The duties and obligations of house surgeons were detailed in the minutes of 1849 which stressed that they should consider their time 'too valuable to be wasted in the gaieties and amusements of the city as heretofore' and a nightly curfew of ten o'clock applied for many years. In the middle of the nineteenth century the Medical Act brought regulation of the profession, and in 1860 house surgeons became paid officers with a salary of £69 a year provided they conducted themselves at all times 'with gentlemanly bearing'. With these restrictions, and no annual leave at all, it could be expected that these junior officers might rebel occasionally. However, the one complaint that was registered most frequently, over a period of many years, was against the rule that junior doctors must eat all meals with the matron.

It was not until 1880 that annual leave was sanctioned for house doctors, but only if they provided – and paid for – their own locums. This system continued until the 1930s. Salaries remained much the same for years, with medical officers receiving slightly more than house surgeons, until the 1920s when surgeons received £150 a year and medical officers only £120. 1925 was a time of general unemployment and it was recorded that fifty doctors had applied for the advertised post for one assistant house surgeon. In that year there was an entry in the minutes referring to the beer allowance that had been granted to resident staff for over a hundred years since the time when water supplies were unsafe. The 1925 entry showed that an enterprising house surgeon used subtle phrasing when he asked for a monthly allowance of £3 'for the purchase of fruit in lieu of beer'. The minutes do not say whether he was successful.

7

Non-Medical Staff

The Head Porter

An entry in the minute books for 1830 lists the porter's numerous duties. They included cleaning the hall, the doorway and the pavement in front of the building, the operating room and the museum. He carried spa water to the hospital from the Hetling supply, and yokes were bought to enable him to carry two leather buckets. He lit fires in each ward, carried coal upstairs and sifted cinders. He also carried patients up and downstairs, alive or dead. For these, and many other responsibilities during fifteen hours of daily duties, he received £12 a year plus his keep, and it is surprising to learn from the minutes that when there was a vacancy many men applied for the post. One porter must have been trying to supplement his wages with a little commercial dealing because the matron reported that he was 'spending too much time making birdcages'.

His main role was as doorkeeper in the early years of the hospital, when he must have been an imposing figure wearing the suit of clothes ordered for him: a claret surtout (his greatcoat), red smallclothes (his breeches), and a hat with a black band. In 1864 several chamois leather skins were specially ordered to make waistcoats for the porter. The many references to his duties quoted in the minute books show that he played an important part in the daily management of the hospital. There was one unfortunate occasion when it was recorded that both the First and Second Porter were unfit for duty due to intoxication. In another entry the surgeons complained that the porter was exceeding his authority by deciding for himself which patients would, or would not, be admitted for treatment. Yet just a few years later, when registration of death had been introduced, it was agreed that if the porter testified he had viewed the body, that could be considered sufficient confirmation of death.

The Surgery Boy

Another member of staff who lived in the hospital was the Surgery Boy, who worked in the operating theatre. In the early years these boys were recruited at the age of twelve or thirteen with a wage of £4 a year plus their keep. They were also given a new suit of clothes every six months, presumably because they were still growing. At that young age they must have witnessed dreadful fear and suffering among surgical patients in the days before the use of anaesthetics.

The Dispenser

When the role of the apothecary changed to that of medical officer, a dispenser of medicines was recruited. In the minute books for 1879 there is a job description submitted by one dispenser hoping for a salary increase:

He attends the hospital at 10am. At 10.30am the Wine Bell is rung and wine delivered to the patients. At 11am dispensing for Out Patients starts... continuing until 8pm when the Dispenser leaves for tea and returns at 9pm to dispense the medicines prescribed by the Resident Medical Officer during morning visits. This takes from one to one and a half hours. On Sundays he attends at 3pm and 9pm.

In addition he must make many of the preparations, tinctures and ointments and this he does by remaining late at night for the purpose. For two days a week he has help from a Dispensary Boy who is considered incompetent.

The plea was successful and the dispenser's salary was raised to £20 a year.

The Hospital Secretary

In the early days of the hospital the matron was responsible for all day-to-day management of the building, but it was recognised that her many duties left little time for nursing administration. Eventually a clerk, known as the Steward and Hospital Secretary, was appointed for the ordering of supplies and for general housekeeping. His responsibilities increased and by the 1870s vacancies for the post, at a salary of £130 a year, were being advertised in The Times, the Naval and Military Gazette, and The Leeds Mercury.

In an attempt to ensure that suitable persons were employed, successful applicants were expected to provide sureties amounting to £300, but unfortunately this was not always a guarantee of honesty. After the death of one secretary it was discovered that £138 had disappeared from the funds, and attempts to claim the £300 surety were not successful. Seven years later, when the replacement secretary also died, the hospital had to pay for his funeral so the Committee felt justified in taking over all the property left in his room. This was listed as: 'Cash £5.10s.0d, some forks and spoons, fifty yards of cloth and three and a half gallons of Scotch whisky.'

Subsequent hospital secretaries proved to be more honourable, were increasingly respected, and by 1900 were paid considerably more than the resident medical staff. An Assistant Hospital Secretary was added to the staff, but in the 1920s, when patients were expected to contribute towards their maintenance in hospital, this post was replaced by that of an Almoner whose duties included the assessment of patients' means and ability to pay.

Domestic Staff

There are no details in the minutes of conditions for domestic staff, except for one entry in 1882. It records a complaint from the hospital laundresses that washing dirty clothes caused them to feel ill, and they were requesting an allowance of brandy one day a week. The Committee thought that tea would be better for them and sent a small supply.

There is no doubt that all hospital staff worked very long hours, and when two weeks annual holiday was eventually allowed, it was usually unpaid leave. The fact that holidays were not taken for granted is shown in an entry in the minute books for 1912 where it was reported that the Hospital Engineer had taken no leave for seventeen years.

The Royal United Hospital Bath.

This photo of the RUH was taken after 1891 when the fourth storey was added onto the earlier building

47

The train that visited various stations raising funds for the RUH

BATH'S NEW HOSPITAL in the green fields and sunshine of Combe Park.

THE ROYAL UNITED HOSPITAL
NEW BUILDINGS AT COMBE PARK, BATH.
H. PERCY ADAMS — A. J. TAYLOR, FRRIBA, ARCHITECTS

The proposed New Royal United Hospital will cost £130,000; the Bath City Council will purchase the present hospital buildings for £30,000; leaving Bath and the district served by the Hospital to raise **£100,000**.

Please send donations to F. G. Hamilton Esq., Hon. Treasurer New Royal United Hospital Appeal Fund, 8 Abbey Churchyard, Bath.

ALL DONATIONS WILL BE DULY ACKNOWLEDGED IN THE PRESS.

The drawing shows a much larger complex than the building that finally opened in 1932

49

An aerial photo of the Combe Park site taken in 1934

8

Diseases and treatments in the Nineteenth Century

The hospital minute books show that every year there were epidemics of potentially fatal diseases.

Smallpox

There was a sixty per cent risk of death in cases of small-pox, and patients who survived were usually permanently scarred. In the early years of the hospital there were attempts to provide an isolation ward, but eventually it was neces-sary to hire outside accommodation during epidemics. In 1850 a house was rented in Chapel Court, part of St John's Hospital, at a cost of £9 to cover a period of six months, but the United Hospital was again in financial trouble. When the owner of the property requested its return, plus back payment of the rent, the Committee had to 'beg his indul-gence' for the remaining patients to be allowed to stay there until they had recovered. Various other houses were rented during later smallpox epidemics, some in St James Parade and one at Green Park. An outbreak in 1858 must have been particularly virulent because it was reported in March that the rented house was proving inadequate for the large number of patients, and it was not until December that the epidemic was finally over.

The severity of that outbreak brought changes for the future. Patients who died were to be buried more promptly and their bedding burnt. According to the records, vaccination had reduced the number of deaths and steps were to be taken to increase its use. Finally in 1879 it was acknowledged that the resident medical officers who treated smallpox patients in their homes may have been spreading infection and carrying it back to the hospital, so it was agreed that there was urgent need for a special fever hospital to be built 'as far from the RUH as possible'.

Cholera

Cholera first came to England in the spring of 1831 in a ship which docked at a port in the north east of the country. Cases were diagnosed at Bristol in 1832 and were seen in Bath within a few days, the majority of them in Avon Street, Dolemeads and Milk Street. To prevent further spread of the epidemic guards were stationed at all roads into the city 'to deter vagrants and travelling mendicants who might be infected'. The Parish Board of the city attempted to start a cholera hospital in various empty premises, but landlords would not cooperate, so a wooden shed on the Upper Bristol Road was used as an isolation house and several people died there, many within 24 hours of the first symptoms of illness.[21]

In the eighteenth and early nineteenth century it was believed that most fevers such as cholera were caused by foul air, and during that first outbreak complaints were sent to the River Company about the amount of filth and offal rotting on the banks of the Avon. Doctors dealing with the cases in Bath realised that cholera was occurring most frequently in over-crowded and insanitary houses, but they were not then aware that it was caused by contaminated drinking water. In the city all clean water piped to houses had to be paid for. The poorer residents who had no taps or wells had to rely on only five free pumps which functioned for a short time each day. One man living in Bath said that his nearest supply of clean water was a quarter of a mile away and was so precious that it was used only for drinking, so all water for washing and cooking came from the river which was 'always muddy and often stinking from the filth it carried'.[22]

In Bath in the 1850s the sewerage system was so inadequate that some houses had permanent walls two or three feet high in front of their doors to prevent sewage flooding in after heavy rain.[23] The local Medical Officer of Health later reported that the River Avon was 'no better than a huge cesspool'.[24] Later government acts enforced slum clearance with improved water supplies and sanitation, and cholera in England was under control by the end of the century.

Treatment

When the Pauper Scheme started in 1747 medical treatments would have been much the same as they had been for previous centuries: herbal remedies and hot or cold poultices were used for everything from sore throats and ear complaints to coughs or colic. For fevers treatment was usually some form of laxative, plus a low diet, often accompanied by blood-letting, and one room at the RUH was known as the Bleeding Room. Specially shaped dishes that fitted round an arm or leg were used to receive the blood which was released by a lancet or with the use of a small box-shaped instrument from which several sharp knives sprang when activated by a lever.

Leeches were an alternative method of reducing the blood supply. In 1824, five million of them were imported into England for medical use.[25] In the RUH minute books for 1831 there was comment on the vast expense of using them for outpatients, and it was then decided that all leeches must be returned to the hospital, alive or dead.

Surgery

A large part of the work of the early surgeons consisted of setting fractures, treating wounds or leg ulcers, and lancing abscesses. If poultices and liniment failed, with infection spreading in a limb amputation was the ultimate solution. But drastic surgery was only undertaken if the patient was certain to die without it. Underneath the wooden operating table a tray filled with sawdust would be pushed by foot to catch the drips of blood from either side of the table. In 1862 the RUH ordered a wooden tray specifically for the removal of amputated limbs from the operating theatre.

A letter was received from Florence Nightingale in 1864 during her campaign for general improvement in standards of medical care. It included 'printed forms' which were to be completed and returned with details of the surgeons and their work, but unfortunately no copies of her letter or the questionnaire were kept with the minutes.

At one meeting in 1887 there was an attempt to regulate the availability of surgical instruments. It was agreed that the House surgeon would be granted £5 a year for taking responsibility to ensure that no instruments were borrowed or taken out of the hospital. However, at the following meeting it was decided that the rule should apply 'except when required by a member of the honorary staff', who presumably might need special instruments for operations on his private patients.

Anaesthesia

Surgical operations were gruesome and terrifying in the days when mandrake root, opium or alcohol were the only means of deadening pain, yet the introduction of anaesthesia in the second half of the century was not at first welcomed by some churchmen, who wrote articles objecting to its use on the principle that pain was sent by God and that some suffering was good for the soul.

The wife of the surgeon Sir James Paget saw and heard much of that suffering in those pre-anaesthesia days when she lived in a house within the grounds of St Bartholomew's Hospital. For many years she was distressed by hearing terrible screams from the nearby operating theatre and, after the introduction of anaesthetics, she felt that one day in each year should be set aside to remember and give special thanks for the research which had resulted in relief for so many people.[26]

Chloroform was first used in England in the 1840s when, because of its numbing effect, it was popularly known as 'sweet whisky' or 'Dutch liquor'.[27] For several years at the RUH the Medical Officer who was responsible for home visits also acted as anaesthetist, but in 1872 a 'chloroformist' was employed at a small salary. Twenty years later an honorary doctor was appointed Administrator of Anaesthetics, and a register was introduced giving details of patients, operations performed and anaesthetics used.[28]

Antisepsis

'The man laid on the operating table in one of our surgical hospitals is exposed to more chance of death than the English soldier on the field of Waterloo'.[29]

Those were the words of the Scottish surgeon Sir James Simpson in 1860. Later in the century surgical risks decreased with the adoption of Joseph Lister's antiseptic techniques, but it took some time before asepsis was achieved in provincial hospitals. Money needed to be spent on new equipment, and in 1885 the surgeons at the RUH asked for a new enamel sink in the operating theatre to replace the wooden one, which was described as 'disgusting and insanitary'. For its stock of surgical instruments the hospital had previously depended on those donated by the widows of previous surgeons and, with handles of wood or ivory, these older types could not be sterilised by boiling.

For many years the Committee dismissed requests for a direct supply of hot water in the operating theatre. It was not until 1892, when Mr Jolly of Milsom Street donated a water heater, that hot water was available. Six years later an entry in the minutes admitted that in the operating theatre the furniture and fittings were 'totally opposed to antiseptic surgery', so £700 was spent on a revised theatre with new instruments. By this time improved arrangements had been made for the disposal of surgical remains. No longer were they buried in the back garden of the hospital, and a register of burial fees for St James' Cemetery in 1876 shows payment for 'a box containing amputated parts of patients from the Royal United Hospital'.

Hygiene reached some parts of the hospital at a slower pace in the 1890s. Management of the mortuary was the responsibility of the head porter, but he was guilty of leaving a body there for ten days. Some time later it seemed advisable to block a door giving access between the hospital kitchen and the mortuary. Things must have improved, however, after doctors were told they must not leave the dissection remains they had been using for research purposes 'lying around in the Museum thus causing noxious smells throughout the building'.

9

Hospital Finance in the Nineteenth Century

Reports on modern NHS hospitals frequently refer to lack of funding and various economies leading to ward closures. But long before the changes that came in 1948, voluntary hospitals all over England had similar problems. For many years they had been financially dependent on the goodwill of the local population, and the money supply varied greatly from year to year.

In the first half of the nineteenth century RUH reports show that annual subscriptions from the wealthier residents of Bath were the main source of income. The majority of these donations were for one guinea, and that sum brought certain privileges such as attendance at annual dinners and annual general meetings. It gave the subscriber the right to vote in ballots to choose the physicians and surgeons for the hospital. It also merited three tickets of recommendation, those pieces of paper vital for hospital treatment. For each church that raised £10 or more some tickets were available, so when destitute people needed to attend the hospital they applied for that Ticket of Relief at the back door of the rectory, at the Squire's house, or at the home of a wealthy person in the community.

This humiliating system existed until the end of the nineteenth century, when there were suggestions that in future all patients should be admitted solely on the recommendation of doctors. But it was said that subscribers enjoyed the patronage and felt that they would lose privilege if the ticket system ended, with the result that donations would cease. Eventually a compromise was reached. Patient admission would be authorised by doctors but those subscribers who still wanted to retain some prestige could send a covering letter of recommendation.

Legacies from wills formed the basis of the hospital's capital with shares in collieries, in new railways and industries, plus investment in India, New Zealand and Jamaica. But legacies were not always straightforward bequests. Some wills stipulated that, in order to benefit, the hospital must be responsible for maintaining graves in good repair. This included painting iron railings, mending stone-work or providing plants and flowers. Six monthly checks at local cemeteries were necessary to ensure maintenance because, if there were complaints that graves were neglected, money from bequests would be transferred to other charities. It is surprising to note that in the 1940s the RUH was still paying money to cemeteries as far away as Hastings and Hove. There was a macabre condition in the will of Mary Harrison who stated that a medical man must certify her as truly dead before her funeral. When she died in 1846 her executor advised George Norman, surgeon at the hospital, to refer to his sense of smell for the 'certification of decomposition before the screwing down'. The hospital received £1200 from the will, the present equivalent of which would be approximately £51,000.

Even with occasional large legacies the hospital frequently had cash flow problems. In 1842 money was lost through the failure of the Hobhouse Bank, so stock to the value of £1500 was sold. There were several later periods when it was necessary to economise by reducing the number of patients treated. In annual reports of the 1880s the first doubts were expressed about the survival of voluntary hospitals that relied purely on public charity.

There were other social changes which affected the hospital. For most of the Victorian age charity was regarded as a Christian duty and religion played an important part in the support of voluntary hospitals, but by the 1890s church donations had greatly diminished. At one annual general meeting of the RUH the Chairman said that the small amounts donated by churches were a disgrace for the city of Bath, and admiration was expressed for 'the working classes who were showing their sense of duty by increased collections'.

The greater percentage of cash was now coming from trades and industries. Various workmen's groups raised money in public houses and, for example, donations from the Somerset Miners' Association were recognised as larger than other contributions. These changes were confirmed by 1902 when delegates from various local firms were appointed to take part in RUH committee meetings, and their influence gradually increased. It was the workers' representatives who wrote to the Mayor saying that the rent the Corporation charged the hospital for use of houses in Hot Bath Street was much too high and should be reduced. They were responsible for changes in visiting days, pointing out that Saturdays were busy times for tradespeople, so Sunday visits were substituted. In 1929, a resolution passed at a meeting of workers strongly opposed the move to Combe Park unless financial support for the new building could be absolutely guaranteed. Later events proved that this would have been a sensible precaution.

Apart from regular money received from annual subscriptions and group contributions, charity came to the hospital in many, often surprising, ways. Sir John Miller was president of the Pauper Charity, and in 1776 he brought back from Italy a very large vase, which he placed in the window of his house at Batheaston. He invited the people of Bath to take part in a poetry competition, entries to be placed in the vase. It was reported that the road to his house was crowded with coaches delivering poems, the best of which were sold to raise funds for the charity. In 1830 the sum of £25 was received from the Duchess of Kent, mother of the future Queen Victoria, and in 1892 Eugenie, the exiled Empress of France, donated £10. Thousands of donors were named in the minute books but some gifts were sent anonymously. Five guineas were sent to the hospital one day with only a covering note to say that they had been 'compensation for slander', and over a period of several years other donations arrived, with the same reason given, so gossip must have been a hazard in Victorian Bath.

When landowners found men poaching they extracted money for the hospital, and witnesses in court cases passed on cash received for expenses. Frequent sums came from penalties imposed by magistrates including fines paid by boatmen for infringement of canal regulations, fines for the two women who were picking flowers in Victoria Park and for the man found fishing in the pond there. It was fortunate for the RUH that charity functions of all kinds were an important part of social life before the coming of cinemas and other forms of commercially based entertainment. Cash was received from the proceeds of the annual Bachelors' Ball, from concerts and from Penny Readings. These were talks given on various subjects, with one penny admittance charge, and the proceeds went to the RUH. Amounts received varied but every one was listed in the minute books, from two shillings raised by carol singers to £1074 from an important Spring Flower Show.

The hospital could not have functioned without those

thousands of donations, large and small, nor could it have managed without the material gifts sent in by every strata of society at different seasons. January shooting parties resulted in gifts of pheasants, partridge and hares in addition to sides of venison received from various landowners. Thousands of eggs were received each spring and each gift was precisely noted in the minutes as, for example, 285 bunches of primroses from the village school in Combe Hay. The longest lists of donations were in autumn when churches sent in huge collections from harvest festivals and, in nearby towns and villages, allotment holders and gardeners took their produce to public houses for delivery to the hospital.

Pictures and jewellery were donated and later sold to raise funds, but the oddest gift was one received in 1885 when Colonel Cross of the 75th Gordon Highlanders sent a collection of heads of Egyptian mummies to his aunt who lived in Bath. She obviously did not know what to do with them – they would not have made attractive ornaments – so she donated them to the hospital. It would be interesting to know where they are now.

10
1900 to 1919

By the turn of the century there had been some changes in administration. The General Purpose Committee remained much the same, with two generals, one lieutenant general, two colonels and one surgeon, but membership had become more democratic with the addition of three well-known names in Bath: Mr Colmer, Mr Jolly and Mr Stothert. Sub-committees had been formed to deal with finance, nursing, and election of staff. The Election Committee now included representatives from various firms and societies such as Bath Gas Company, Somerset Miners and Bath Cycling Club, a group of enthusiasts on penny-farthings who raised consider-able sums of money for the hospital through bicycle cavalcades and carnivals.

The commitment of the hospital had altered considerably during the nineteenth century because other institutions had opened to offer medical treatment for the poorer people of the city. Bath Eye Infirmary was founded in 1811, the Walcot Ear and Eye Infirmary followed in 1837, and cottage hospitals had opened in outlying districts. An entry in the minutes in 1848 said that 'paralytic patients', a term which usually referred to those with joint disease, would now be admitted to the General Hospital (later called the Mineral Water Hospital) where treatment by electricity was available. Patients with minor illness received medicines at the three local Dispensaries, and the Fever Hospital (also known as the

Statutory Hospital) accepted cases of smallpox, scarlet fever, diphtheria and typhoid. Because these other services existed, the role of the hospital gradually changed from that of an institution which catered only for destitute patients and a great range of diseases, to one offering more specialised treatment, not only for the poorest of patients, but including paid workers who had some form of insurance.

An important change in administration was noted in the minute books. The hospital had for many years received much practical help from the Ladies Working Association which raised funds, sent gifts of food and supplied all linen, blankets, etc. Each member undertook to sew at least two articles of clothing each year for patients ('machined garments not accepted') and it was recorded that the association provided thousands of items annually. Despite all these efforts, requests for representation were refused by the Committee, which recorded that it was 'against the inclusion of females'. However, at the open Annual General Meeting held at the Guildhall in 1905, an ultimatum was received from a Mrs Hallet. She said 'The constitution of this hospital is ancient and needs complete revision' and threatened that women would withdraw all help if shut out of management. In January 1906 it was agreed that women could be nominated for vacancies on the Board.

Finance

One feature of the hospital never changed. Every January the President of the hospital board made an appeal to the public for more annual subscriptions and donations. In 1901 it was reported that unless funding increased, 'as far as Bath was concerned, hospitals supported by voluntary contribution were a failure', and at the RUH many drastic economies were necessary. Home visits were reduced by fifty per cent, and patients who could afford to pay something towards their keep were charged a sum of two guineas for maintenance. This was considered to be a better system than at Bristol Royal Infirmary where patients were charged for tea, eggs and sugar.

For many years the hospital had relied on money from legacies. However, in 1909 it was said that they had decreased considerably in the previous ten years, from an expectation of £1000 a year (approximately £48,000 at present rates) to only £66.10s, so the deficit at the RUH increased. The introduction of Lloyd George's National Insurance Bill in 1911 should therefore have been welcome, because it ensured that all workers (and their employers) contributed regular sums for treatment, but at the hospital there was anxiety about possible state interference. There was also fear that the public would no longer regard the hospital as a charity and donations would decrease. This certainly happened in some cases. For example, Lord Waldegrave, who owned local mines, sent a letter saying that in view of the new insurance scheme he would no longer subscribe. He later relented (his mines were still submitting tenders for supply of coal to the hospital) and he agreed to send a reduced sum of two guineas.

Changes in treatment

The rapid advances in medicine and science during the second half of the nineteenth century had brought many changes in medical care. The introduction of anaesthesia meant that surgeons could spend more time on operations and patients were less terrified of undergoing surgery. Statistics given in 1905 show that, compared with ten years before, nearly four times as many operations were being done annually at the RUH. New surgical instruments, which could be sterilized by boiling, had been bought to replace the older types with wood or ivory handles. The use of antiseptic methods, together with improvement in nursing and general cleanliness, meant that new operations, including abdominal surgery, could be carried out with greater hope of success. In the annual reports of this period it was claimed that operations performed at the RUH were well in advance of those done in America.

There was greater emphasis on diagnosis. In Bath, interest in pathology had begun in the 1870s, but it was not until the turn of the century that space was set aside for the Bacteriology Laboratory. An entry in the minutes for 1896 mentioned X-Ray as 'skiagraphy' or the 'New Photography', and a legacy was used to buy Roentgen rays at a cost of £70. A year later a coil (to give a fifteen inch spark) was bought for £30. At first the apparatus shared the Anaesthetic Room, but in 1905 a separate Electrical Department was formed. For several years there were constant references to the cost of X-Ray used for the treatment of hundreds of cases of ringworm, and at that time there was no reference in the minute books to any form of safety precautions in radiography. When there was a shortage of experienced staff it was agreed that X-Ray photography could be done by any untrained person, and the first mention of risk was in 1920 when a protective rubber apron was ordered.

Buildings

Rapid growth in population and improvements in medical care meant that more space was needed. In 1889 the hospital had acquired rooms in No.3 Hot Bath Street and, a few years later, several adjacent houses were rented from the Corporation. According to the annual report for 1908, these houses gave 'suitable and sanitary accommodation' for the matron and nurses, plus a new outpatient department and a small isolation ward. Some renovations were necessary in the main part of the hospital. For example, there was need to replace the only lift in the building. The original hydraulic mechanism had never been satisfactory because three men were needed to pump the water from a well in the basement, but it was useful for 'carrying coal in the morning, dinners a little later... and sometimes patients'. For several years Stothert and Pitt, the hospital engineers, had issued warnings about its defects and, despite the addition of 'a sliding door to the lift instead of present curtains', it had been a hazard for many years. It was finally replaced in 1912 by an electric lift financed by H O Wills of the Bristol tobacco company.

There were other safety precautions that needed improvement in the new century. There was an unusual entry in the minutes of 1891 referring to the purchase of hand grenades. These were glass phials, filled with chemicals to be thrown from a distance onto burning material to extinguish the fire, but it seems they were not completely efficient because a few months later there was mention of fire damage in the hospital and it was necessary to order life lines. These two inch wide manilla ropes were to be kept near the window of each ward for emergency exit but, for elderly or disabled patients, it would certainly have proved difficult to abseil down the walls of that tall building. Eventually fire escapes were installed on both east and west sides of the hospital but they did not extend to the children's ward above the Albert Wing in the highest part of the building. This was remedied by Arthur Stanley Wills who raised an appeal to provide money for a third iron staircase.

It was reported in 1913 that the drain from the mortuary was choked, that lavatories and other drains were not working, and this was the period when there were several cases of typhoid in the wards.

In 1915 there were several improvements in the operating theatre to give better ventilation, and radiators were installed to replace the old stove which had been sited in the middle of the room, but there were no more improvements for some time afterwards because costs of food and supplies had started to rise soon after the declaration of war.

War 1914 – 1918

From entries in the minute books it seems that the management board of the hospital was almost unaware of the patriotic enthusiasm that was sweeping the country at the start of the First World War. Other institutions had obviously been making preparations for an emergency, such as the Red Cross and St John's Ambulance Brigade. For several years they had been training young women for wartime nursing in groups called Voluntary Aid Detachments. Teaching usually took place in church halls or private houses. A few months before the outbreak of war, the hospital received letters from two Red Cross divisions asking if these trainee nurses (always individually known as VADs) could attend the RUH for ward experience.

The first recorded mention of war in the minutes was when a letter was received from Bristol Royal Infirmary with a request that, in view of the fact that nearly all of its own accommodation had been offered for use by the army, the RUH would admit Bristol patients if necessary. In reply, the Hospital stated that space was limited and all beds would be needed for Bath cases. A few days later the Royal Army Medical Corps in Salisbury wrote asking how many beds would be available for the army. Dr Bannatyne, Senior Physician at the RUH, suggested that 90 beds could be reserved, but because the Mineral Water Hospital had already offered 220 beds for military casualties, the RUH management board decided there was no need to act. In November 1914 it was agreed that 25 Belgian army casualties could be admitted for a few days, although at that time there were no plans to accept British serving men.

Many appeals came from the War Office asking for the admittance of serving wounded soldiers, but only one or two cases of disabled, pensioned soldiers were admitted for treatment, and it was not until much later that some beds were found for serving soldiers. This lack of cooperation was probably a financial decision. The RUH was a voluntary hospital, and short of funds. The amount paid by the army of 2s 6d per day for each serving soldier was too low to cover costs, but the War Pensions Committee paid four shillings a day for discharged soldiers.

The RUH Annual Report for 1916 began with the statement that it had been a quiet year for the hospital, but in other places it had been an eventful year. The Battle of the Somme started in July and on the first day 19,000 British soldiers died and over 35,000 were seriously wounded. Some of the casualties arrived in Bath five days later to be treated at the Bath War Hospital. This new hospital was not in any way connected with the RUH but was maintained by the War Office with the help of the people of Bath. Planning had started in 1915 when the Mayor, Frederick Spear, received a telegram from the Royal Army Medical Corps in Salisbury asking if Bath could provide 500 beds for war casualties. Ten long wooden huts were built for what was to become the first hospital on the Combe Park site. An operating theatre and X-Ray rooms were donated by a committee raised by the Mayor, and Cedric Chivers (owner of the book binding firm) donated an electro-therapeutic block fitted with the latest physiotherapy equipment, including a whirlpool bath.

Dr Bannatyne, who had frequently suggested that more beds should be provided for soldiers, left the RUH and became Lieut. Colonel G A Bannatyne, Commandant of the War Hospital. Many general practitioners in Bath volunteered to assist the medical staff, and Red Cross VADs were employed to assist the trained nurses and medical orderlies. The sum paid by the War Office for maintenance and treatment of soldiers eventually was raised to three shillings, which covered only about half of the actual cost, but £30,000 came from public subscription due to the efforts of Walter Mallet, the hospital Treasurer. Local people donated vast quantities of food and, in kitchens that eventually catered for nearly a thousand patients, all staff were local volunteers.

The first patients were accepted at the War Hospital in May 1916, but the number of casualties rapidly increased. More beds were put into existing wards and by 1917 it was necessary for large marquees to be erected in the grounds of the hospital to accommodate another 600 beds. Auxiliary hospitals opened for small numbers of casualties in Bath, Bathampton and Bradford-on-Avon, all under the administration of the War Hospital, which finally had responsibility for over 1400 beds.

In the meantime the RUH was coping with a shortage of supplies, rising costs and the necessity to insure the hospital against damage by zeppelins, but staff shortage was the greatest problem. Soon after war started several doctors volunteered for service with the Royal Army Medical Corps (RAMC) and some did not return. Some, like the anaesthetist G H Almond and the surgeon Forbes Fraser, returned from military duties to work for a few months at the hospital, but were recalled to the army in France. Mr Forbes Fraser survived but Dr Almond died on active service. In July 1917, when only seven doctors remained out of the usual complement of seventeen, the hospital appealed to Lloyd George requesting that two medical men who had received call up papers could have deferment from military service, but this was refused. At one point it was suggested in committee that a female resident medical officer could be appointed, but there was a decision that 'it was not desirable to appoint a Lady as House Physician' and that it would be preferable to have the services of a male senior medical student.

There are only two entries in the minute books indicating that there was any contact or liaison between the RUH and the War Hospital. In 1917, unable to cope with the extra large convoys of sick or wounded men, the War Hospital asked for help and for a few weeks twenty beds were added to the normal average of ninety at the RUH. One month before the Armistice was signed there was another appeal. This time the management board agreed that it was necessary to accommodate as many casualties as possible, so with the help of bedsteads, mattresses and five extra nurses supplied by the War Office, forty three soldiers were admitted.

Convoys of casualties continued to arrive at the War Hospital, the last of which was recorded on 30th June, seven months after the end of the war.[30] Eventually, fewer immediate casualties were received there so the hospital catered for chronic cases or cases of severe disablement and, in 1922, changed its name to the Ministry of Pensions Hospital.

Dr Bannatyne and Mr Forbes Fraser returned to work at the RUH, together with Walter Mallet to deal with finance, and almost immediately all three were involved in plans to extend the medical services there.

11
1920 to 1939

The limitations of the original hospital building had been recognised for a long time. Forty years before the First World
War it had been suggested that, to combat infection, there
was need for an extension to be built 'on high ground above
the city'. In 1919, when it was known that the War Office
would eventually relinquish the site of the Pensions (War)
Hospital at Combe Park, plans were made to expand the services of the RUH by building four separate medical units
there.

It seems incredible that a hospital in financial difficulties
would attempt to raise the necessary funds for such an
ambitious scheme, but associated with the hospital at that
time there was a small group of dedicated men who were
determined to reduce RUH debts and gain money for
expansion. Soon after the Armistice they applied to various
institutions for the residue of funds raised during the war.
£12,000 was granted from the wartime National Relief Fund
and £4,000 came from surplus monies previously held by the
War Hospital. The Headquarters of the Red Cross had felt it
necessary to admonish the RUH for its lack of cooperation in
the training of VAD nurses during the war, but three years
later when Forbes Fraser and Walter Mallet visited the
society to exhibit plans for the private hospital, £17,000 was
granted for the new building.

That unit would be for 'persons of modest means' who

could not afford the fees of private nursing homes but could pay a smaller amount towards both maintenance and treatment in what was to be the Royal United Private Hospital. Accommodation was also needed for the special treatment of children crippled by diseases like polio and rickets, so an open-air unit was planned to accept patients from a large area. This was to be named 'The Bath, Somerset, Dorset and Wiltshire Children's Orthopaedic Hospital'.

The third unit was planned to offer a much needed maternity service. The city council and various charities had for many years given aid to pregnant women, with the majority of infants being born at home, but when it was necessary for difficult maternity cases to be admitted to the RUH, labour took place in the general medical wards.

It was also suggested that there should be a convalescent home on the site and, as the hospital was at this time running on a deficit of £13,000, it was necessary to appeal to the public for what was known as the Extension Fund.

In the early 1920s there were no plans to move the rest of the hospital from the original building in the city and efforts were made towards modernization there. Oil lamps and hand held lanterns were recognised as fire hazards and were replaced by gas or electricity. In the wards, open fires were replaced by gas fires and, in 1925, there was an installation of wireless made possible by numerous sets of surplus earphones donated by local families who were beginning to use the modern loudspeaker systems.

Before 1920 there were only a few references in the minutes to any form of rehabilitation or physiotherapy. The first occasion was in 1838 when 'a wooden tube and pulley' were ordered for exercising weak arms, and towards the end of the 1890s third year nurses could, at their own cost, receive training in massage. It was not until 1920 that a full time masseuse was appointed and a physiotherapy department opened.

From then on the records include rapidly rising statistics for patients receiving massage, 'artificial sunlight' or other electrical treatment, and a room in the basement was used for 'children's exercises'.

But modernization could not help all parts of the old hospital. Rats, mice and cockroaches were 'a great nuisance'. In 1925 there was a serious outbreak of scarlet fever. The masseuse died, other staff were affected, and for several weeks the hospital was closed to all visitors. By this time it was acknowledged that the old building was 'sunless... difficult to ventilate and any attempts to provide extra air and sunshine for patients on lead roofs or tiny iron balconies were pitiful'. So plans were made for the whole hospital to be included in the Combe Park scheme.

There was much unemployment immediately after the First World War. There was the general strike of 1926, and towards the end of the 1920s the country was affected by the great financial depression. Yet the impression gained from hospital records and local newspapers is that the people of Bath and the surrounding districts responded eagerly to special appeals for their hospital. There were flag days, flower shows, displays of hairdressing, gymnastic demonstrations, pigeon races, a motor carnival and many other ingenious ways of raising large or (very frequently) small amounts.

Once again local residents responded to the needs of children, and the orthopaedic hospital opened to treat the first few patients in April 1924. With no previously allocated lump sum for its construction, all funds for the orthopaedic hospital came from charity, from individual cash donations, from organised functions and from house-to-house collections in towns and villages over a large area. The number of beds rapidly increased, and several years later when older patients were admitted for treatment, the original lengthy title was abbreviated to The Bath and Wessex Ortho-paedic Hospital.

The Royal United Private Hospital also opened in 1924 but there was tragedy when, two weeks before the opening date, Forbes Fraser died from septicaemia contracted through his surgical work. In recognition of all that he had done to establish the unit, it was renamed the Forbes Fraser Extension of the Royal United Hospital.

Plans for a maternity hospital and convalescent home were shelved when it was decided to move the main hospital from the city. But the hospital could not be moved while the Pensions Hospital was still caring for a large number of sick or wounded soldiers. In fact, the former war hospital was still in use until 1929 (eleven years after the Armistice) when the few remaining patients were moved to a military hospital at Chepstow. In the meantime, the RUH acquired more land at Combe Park – and added to its overdraft – so a new system of fund raising was organised, known as the Mayor of Bath's £100,000 Appeal. The printed appeal forms stressed the defects of the old city building, including 'sanitary arrange-ments hopelessly out of date ... congestion in all departments ... and deplorable provision for nurses and staff.' These were contrasted with 'the advantage of healthy surroundings in the green fields and sunshine of Combe Park'.

Hundreds of fundraising events were recorded in the minutes or in the press, and some were more successful than others. There were hopes for £220 from a proposed mile of pennies to be laid next to the curb through the city but only half a mile was completed, and a more ambitious mile of sil-ver coins did not get very far. Plans were made for a lottery with two cars, a new Hillman valued at £305 and a Triumph worth £169, as the main prizes. Unfortunately there were complaints from some churches, so the lottery was banned and it was recorded in the newspapers that the city of Bath had 'thus been saved from moral danger'.

Other plans were more successful. There was a swimming gala where Miss Forrester Brown, surgeon at the orthopaedic hospital, gave a diving demonstration. At a big fête in Victoria Park a team of St Bernard dogs collected money in miniature barrels, and some people in Bath remember taking a penny to school once a week to buy 'bricks' for the hospital. These were strips of gummed brown paper on which the child's name was written and placed on a board representing a growing brick wall. Over £60 was raised when a train from Fry's chocolate factory was in Bath for two days with exhibits of chocolate boxes and their contents. In April 1934 the hospital was promised ten per cent of the proceeds of an air pageant where the Sky Devils' Air Circus performed aerial stunts. Short flights for passengers cost 3s 6d and the public were also allowed to inspect the interior of an Imperial Airways Argosy with space for 28 passengers – an impressive sight at that time.

Several owners of large firms in Bath, such as Cedric Chivers, James Colmer and Percy Stothert, were named as generous subscribers to the appeal. By far the largest amounts came from Stanley Wills. For the start of the appeal he promised to pay £10,000 if the people of Bath could produce £90,000 within six months. This proved impossible but he still donated the pledged sum. A year later he offered a similar amount if the public could raise £15,000 within six months. Renewed efforts and more charity functions raised only £8,000 to which Stanley Wills added £10,000, and he gave more in following years. In these days, with current awareness of the health risks associated with smoking, it is strange to think that such a large portion of the RUH building was only made possible with money donated by a tobacco company. When Stanley Wills died in February 1935 the hospital received £30,000 from his will with the proviso that, if the RUH ever became a state aided institution, income from the legacy must go instead to the Mayor of Bristol.

The architect's drawings for the proposed new hospital show a large complex, but lack of money meant that only about seventy per cent of the planned building was completed. The old hospital building in town was sold to Bath Corporation for £30,000 and was used later by Bath Technical College.

The first patients were moved to Combe Park in November 1932 and the new hospital must have seemed airy and spacious after the confines of the city building. Gardens were landscaped (with trees donated by the arboretum at Westonbirt) and the men who worked there, under the Mayor's scheme to relieve unemployment, received a gift of 'clogs and warm socks'. But there must have been some disappointment about the new building. A year after the opening it was recorded that, although £150,000 had been spent, the hospital was 'overcrowded with 160 patients'. Four of the wards had not been equipped and there were two hundred patients on the waiting list. Lack of space meant that some of the War Hospital wooden huts had to be retained for nurse accommodation, a laboratory, the X-Ray department and an operating theatre.

The hospital still relied on charitable offerings of all kinds, and Bath Record Office has a gift book listing items sent in to the hospital by the public between 1933 and 1939. Gifts included collections of silver paper received from children whose names were recorded, numerous sheets or pillow cases, and vast quantities of fruit and vegetables, much of which came from the garden of Haile Selassie, Emperor of Abyssinia, who lived in Weston at that time. Annual Pound Days brought in many pounds of meat, jam, butter or sugar, and donors could place orders with local tradesmen for deliveries to the hospital. Local beekeeping societies sent honey, and each spring eggs were donated in large quantities. In 1934, for example, 9300 eggs were received over a period of eleven days, and many of them were stored in isinglass for use in winter. The number of gifts decreased towards the end of 1939 and were infrequent during the following years of war.

12

War 1939 to 1945

Six years after the hospital opened at Combe Park another war was imminent, but this time preparations had been made. In January 1938 plans were formed for the evacuation of patients from the East Block, which in the case of war would become the Fourth Southern Territorial Army Hospital for the treatment of military casualties and also for civilians injured through enemy action. It was staffed by doctors from the RUH as part time soldiers, with a commanding officer, a quartermaster, and twenty four additional recruits. These included Miss Vian, matron of the RUH, who resigned her duties there to become Principal Matron of the territorial unit.

To release more space for the emergency, nurses were moved from their wooden accommodation to 157 Newbridge Hill where three nearby air raid shelters were provided for them. Soon after war was declared, trenches were dug in the hospital grounds to provide emergency cover for nursing staff attempting to reach the main building during air raids. Day nurses were on call at the hospital one night in six for air raid duty and were expected to be back on day duty at 9am. Other staff were on call as plane spotters or fire fighters and there were appeals for voluntary stretcher bearers.

Notices were posted stressing that treatment would be refused for any patient arriving at the hospital without a gas mask, and a Gas Decontamination Block was built where contaminated clothes could be removed and patients 'scrubbed down'. The hospital's eight hundred windows were treated with anti-splinter paint, which was applied by volunteer masters and boys from Beechen Cliff School, and gummed strips of paper were also attached to all windows as an anti-blast precaution. There were plans to grow vegetables in the hospital grounds and five hundred tons of coal were ordered to be stored in case of future shortage.

For the first few months of war the Territorial Army medical unit functioned on the site and East Block was available for both local and military patients, but in March 1940 the War Office compulsorily requisitioned the space to be used for military personnel only. It was to be a temporary arrangement until such time as hutted accommodation could be built for a regular military hospital. However, according to letters and notes in the minutes, the take-over was much against the wishes of both the Territorial Army Command at Salisbury and of staff at the RUH who resented the loss of beds for civilians. The situation became even more difficult in the autumn of 1940 when the hospital was accepting air raid casualties from other parts of the country.

Entries in the minutes show that there was also resentment at some loss of finance, and for several months efforts were made to recoup money already spent on providing facilities for the army. In 1941 Aubrey Bateman, Mayor of Bath and President of the hospital, finally delivered an ultimatum:

> No money having been received from the War Office
> since January this hospital is unable to meet its commit-
> ments unless £10,000 is sent by return.

£5,000 was received but efforts to recover the whole amount continued for some time.

There are only brief notes in the minutes covering the

terrible bombing of Bath on the nights of 25th and 26th April 1942 and its effects on the hospital, but they are enough to indicate that running an efficient medical service must have been a nightmare. The Mineral Water Hospital had been designated a Casualty Clearing Station for the distribution of patients to other hospitals, but it was damaged in the first raid, and received direct bomb damage the following night, so was unable to assist.

In comparison, structural damage to the RUH building was comparatively minor, although many windows were blown out and no electricity could be used for lighting because blackout material had been damaged. The gas supply failed for two weeks and water pressure was practically nil, so Leicestershire Yeomanry Mobile Tanks provided supplies of fresh water with the help of pumps from the local fire brigade. Hurricane lamps replaced electricity and cooking was done on petrol or paraffin stoves. The nurses' home on Newbridge Hill received more serious damage and was unfit for accommodation, so nurses were housed in various places locally.

Over two days, 147 casualties were admitted to an already overcrowded hospital, but help came from many sources. A central emergency surgical team came from Bristol and staff came from the Bristol Royal Infirmary; there was help from the Field Ambulance Service of the Royal Air Force and also from many family doctors.

Fortunately the War Office had released the bed space in East Block when the new huts were nearing completion a few weeks before the raids began but, less than a year later, an American contingent was occupying the military site. Several local people remember American soldiers in the area but there is no reference in the minute books to the arrival of 152 United States Station Hospital (Florida) and no information is available at the Record Office, so it seems that siting this unit at Combe Park was an arrangement just between the War Office and the United States Military Authority. There is a brief note of the American hospital's existence in 1943, when it was said that the decontamination of gas casualties was in future to be undertaken by that unit, and again in June 1945 when the single storey buildings, no longer occupied by the US military authority, were released by the War Office for use by the RUH. That part of the Combe Park site was opened for patients in September 1948 and was known as the Manor Hospital.

13

National Health Service

It was during the war that plans were made to modify the system of health insurance which had been introduced in 1911. Without the regular income it brought, many voluntary hospitals would not have been able to carry on as long as they did. But that structure of insurance did not cover all the population; the wives and children of working men were not included, nor was there provision in the scheme for elderly or disabled persons. In the 1930s some political groups were campaigning for reform, stressing the need for a state medical service, because it was felt that a two-tier system had evolved where those who could afford something towards hospital costs were receiving better treatment. This campaigning resulted in the Beveridge Scheme, which recommended compulsory insurance to cover all social services including medical treatment.

Hospital administrative boards had always expressed doubts about state intervention, and at the RUH there was reluctance to accept government handouts because consultants would no longer give their services free if hospitals were not classed as charities. General practitioners felt that under a state-run system they would lose freedom to treat their patients in the way they thought best and, in an opinion poll taken at the time, they voted eight to one against the scheme.

The Ministry of Health tried to quell all doubts with the statement that:

...there were many mistaken ideas that the proposals would turn the medical profession into some sort of State-controlled and regimented service and ruin the voluntary health movement. Nothing could be further from the truth than to suppose that the Government intended either of these things to happen.[31]

An association of voluntary hospitals replied to this in a pamphlet stating that the medical profession would cooperate with the Ministry of Health to provide the best hospital service for the whole community, but that there was 'strong disagreement with the Government's intention to confiscate funds, buildings, investments and equipment at a cash value of £3,000,000,000 in hospitals over the country'. It added that the system would 'discourage the public from showing sympathy or interest in hospitals and would substitute bureaucratic control for local enthusiasm'.[32]

There was a public debate at the Guildhall in Bath in 1945 when it was said that 'health should never be regarded as a political issue', but the scheme was approved. In October 1947 all voluntary hospitals were officially transferred to the Ministry of Health to become part of the National Health Service, which, by Order of Council, came into effect on 5th July 1948.

The RUH was no longer a voluntary institution. For years it had struggled to retain its independence, relying greatly on financial help from the general public. At a meeting in 1927 it was said that there were very few households in Bath and in the surrounding villages which did not have a collecting box holding small sums for the hospital. The various fund raising events and functions played an important part in the social life of the community, but unfortunately the amounts raised were never enough to cover the cost of new and expensive treatment for an increasing population.

Depression in the 1930s and the costs of war made it obvious that some other form of regular financial backing was essential and it seemed that this could only come with state involvement. Perhaps some of the doubts and misgivings expressed about the National Health in the 1940s may now seem justified, but it is not true that the public has been discouraged from showing sympathy and interest in the RUH. There are many of us who have reason to be proud of our hospital and grateful for its services.

Appendix A
Chronology

1747   Pauper Charity formed for dispensing medicine to destitute people of the city.

1792   The Pauper Charity moved to new premises and changed its name to City Infirmary and Dispensary.

1788   Casualty Hospital founded at 38 Kingsmead Street.

1823   The United Hospital is formed; a union of the Casualty Hospital and the City Infirmary.

1826   Bath United Hospital opened in new building at Beau Street.

1827   First volume of minutes of the management committee.

1832   First cholera epidemic in Bath.

1862   Nurse Training Institute formed.

1864   Albert Wing extension to the existing building. Roman remains uncovered.

1868   Permission granted by Queen Victoria for the change of name to Royal United Hospital.

1877   Widcombe Bridge Disaster.

1880   Fever Hospital opened at Claverton.

1888   Residential Nurse Training School opened.

1893   Box Tunnel Railway accident.

1896   Lectures and examinations for nurses.
        Rooms in Hot Bath Street rented for extra
        accommodation.
        First reference to X-Ray at RUH.

1916   Bath War Hospital established.

1920   RUH bought land at Combe Park.

1924   Expansion of RUH services with the opening of two
        units, the Forbes Fraser RUH Private Hospital and
        the orthopaedic hospital for children.

1929   War Hospital (Pensions Hospital) closed.

1931   Sale of Beau Street building for later use of Bath
        Technical College.

1932   Patients moved from the city to Combe Park.

1939   RUH Territorial Medical Unit established.

1940   East Block of hospital requisitioned by War Office.

1942   Air raids on Bath.
        American hospital on part of RUH site.

1945   American hospital buildings released, later known as
        Manor Hospital.

1947   All voluntary hospitals transferred to Ministry of
        Health.

1948   National Health Service came into effect in July.

Appendix B
The Roman Pavement

The Roman pavement was discovered in 1864 during the excavation of the foundations for the extension to the hospital and, over the next thirty-three years, efforts were made to preserve it in situ. In 1897 the Roman Baths Museum opened and the following extract shows that there were plans for the pavement to be moved there:

> Resolved that it be referred to the Surveyor of Works to prepare for placing the antiquities in the new museum in the Roman Promenade. In reply to a question by Mr Councillor Oliver, the Chairman stated that spaces had been reserved on the floor of the Museum for the Roman pavement from the Weymouth House School and Royal United Hospital.
>
> *From City of Bath Council and Committee*
> *Minutes: 19th November 1897 (p.512)*

The transfer did not take place and the following extracts from the RUH minute books covering the period 1864-1897 seem to indicate that the pavement had deteriorated to such an extent that removal was not feasible.

8th August 1864: A letter was received from Mr Gill, the Architect, respecting the Roman Remains discovered in the excavation. It was resolved to accept his offer of the photographs, and to defer consideration of the other part of his letter until next Monday in consequence of the discovery this morning of further remains.

15th August 1864: Mr J.E. Gill submitted, for the inspection of the Board, a tracing, full size, of the tessellated pavement discovered last week. It was resolved that the pavement be preserved in situ. Mr Gill also produced sundry Roman articles which were ordered to be carefully preserved in the Hospital Museum.

18th November 1867: In answer to a letter from Mr Murch, the Chairman of the Literary Institution requesting the loan to the Institution of the Roman remains found on the site of the hospital, it was resolved that the Remains be sent on the conditions proposed, viz: as a deposit to be returned to the hospital at any time if requested.

18th May 1868: The "Roman Remains" room to be attended to.

30th August 1869: The Roman Pavement is going fast to decay and it was resolved that Mr Irving (sic) be spoken to on the subject.

21st October 1872: Mr Elkington Gill, the architect, attended the Board and made a Report on the state of the Roman Bath and the Secretary was directed to write a note to the Rev. A.H. Winwood requesting him to meet the sub-committee (appointed last week) and the Architect on Wednesday next, the 23 inst at 10.30 o'clock, to consult as to the means of preserving it from decay. The Architect was instructed to carry out his suggestions for repairing the roof over the Roman Bath.

4ᵗʰ November 1872: Architect's letter dated 2ⁿᵈ November 1872 stated 'A small portion of the hypocaust has fallen in. £50 needed for safe keeping.'

One sentence written on the back of the letter (presumably by a clerk or member of the committee) stated 'Regret that there were no hospital funds to apply to the improvements suggested.'

21ˢᵗ September 1874: Messrs Gill and Brown, the architects, presented a report on the state of the Arch above the Roman Bath, accompanied by an Estimate from Mr Bladwell of the cost of carrying out their suggestions amounting to £22.5.0d. or with a new brick arch to £33.5.0d. The matter was referred to the Sub Committee... to meet on Wednesday next, the 23rd inst at 10 o'clock and consult with the Architect.

28ᵗʰ September 1874: The Sub Committee... inspected the arch roof of the Roman Bath and recommended that a grating 18inches square be placed in the South Wall and that the Architect's report on the repairs necessary, including the erection of a new brick arch (£32.5.0d.) should be carried out as the most satisfactory course.

5ᵗʰ October 1874: The Committee inspected the Roman Bath and, after discussion, it was resolved that the Architect's Report of the repairs necessary be adopted and carried out at an expense of £22.5.0d., this being the amount of Mr Bladwell's tender.

15ᵗʰ August 1878: Letter – difficulties with damp.

19ᵗʰ August 1878: It was resolved that, as far as the ventilation portion of the report was concerned, the repairs would be carried out by Mr Bladwell under the superintendence of Messrs Gill and Brown.

26th August 1878: Suggestion to fill in with dry rubbish or concrete up to 8-10" of joist.

9th September 1880: The Secretary reported that a portion of the Roman Remains on the hospital premises showed signs of decay and required repairing.

18th October 1880: Lt.Col St Aubyn as Treasurer of the Bath Natural History and Antiquarians Field Club stated that the club was willing to subscribe from their funds towards repairs.

14th July 1897: Proposed that the Roman pavement under the Officers' quarters be offered to the Town Council to be removed at their own expense.

Appendix C
Resources

At Bath Record Office:

RUH Minute Books, volumes 1-19, covering period 1827-1929;

Minute books for various committees and sub committees 1840-1929;

Surgical In-patients' Book 1891-1895;

Anaesthetics and Operations Book 1891-1898;

Albums of press cuttings covering 1917-1951;

Gift Book – for material donations – 1933-1939.

At Bath Central Library

RUH Annual Reports (Year Books) 1851-1937;

Bath Guides and Directories 1755-

Authors note: Apart from where otherwise noted in the text, all material comes from RUH records. Many direct quotes from committee meetings have been used because they give an indication of the times in which they were written. In an attempt to limit lists of dates within the text, these quotes have not been individually referenced. However, a chronological list of all items noted from the minutes is available in the Record Office together with a comprehensive list of sources used.

Notes

1   Pamphlet 3621 BA 602 176, AGM Pauper Charity, Bath Central Library.

2   Bath and County Graphics 1901, pp95-6.

3   Poster 103, Pauper Scheme 1771 (from Broadsheets and Posters), Bath Central Library.

4   New Bath Guide, 1766.

5   G. Munro Smith, *History of Bristol Royal Infirmary*, Arrowsmith Ltd., Bristol, 1917.

6   Letter to the Mayor from James Norman, 1820, Bath Records Office.

7   Barry Cunliffe, *Roman Remains Discovered*, Routledge and Kegan Paul, 1971

8   Paget, Stephen, *Memoirs and Letters of Sir James Paget*, Longmans, Green & Co., 1901.

9   Cecil Woodham Smith, *Florence Nightingale*, Constable, 1950.

10 Broadsheets and Posters, Poster No.103, Bath Central Library.

11 Reader, W.J., *Life in Victorian England*, Batsford, 1964.

12 Marsh C.A., *Early Medical Practice in Bath*, in "Bristol Medical Chirurgical Journal", October 1964.

13 Digby, Anne : Making a Medical Living 1994

14 Glaser, S., *The Spirit of Inquiry, Caleb Hillier Parry, MD,FRS*, Alan Sutton Publishing Ltd, 1995.

[15] Volpe, R. *The Endocrinologist,* Vol 4(3), May 1994

[16] *ibid.*

[17] Wright, R.W., Director of Bath Library Authority 1948.

[18] Mainwaring, R, 'Epidemic in Bath 1832', Bath Central Library.

[19] Chapters from the life of Eliza Day as told to W. Parker, *Weston Village Journal*, Mushroom Publishing, 1999.

[20] G. Munro Smith, *History of Bristol Infirmary*, Arrowsmith Ltd, Bristol, 1917

[21] Mainwaring, R. (Secretary to the Board of Health), 'Epidemic in Bath', published 1833. Bath Central Library.

[22] Reader, W.J., *Life in Victorian England*, Batsford, 1964.

[23] Mitchell, W. J., from a pamphlet entitled, 'Short Statement of Engineer's Works 1849-1885'.

[24] Brabazon, A.B., Medical Officer of Health, Bath 1888.

[25] Kingscote-Davies, Eastbourne Medical Gazette 1980, p.154.

[26] Paget, Stephen, *Memoirs and Letters of Sir James Paget*, Longmans Green & Co., 1901, p.183.

[27] Cameron, J R, *Journal of Royal College of Surgeons of Edinburgh*, January 1971, vol.16(1).

[28] RUH Anaesthetics and Operations Book 1891-1898, Bath Record Office.

[29] Cameron, J R, *Journal of Royal College of Surgeons of Edinburgh*, January 1971, vol.16(1).

[30] *Bath Guide 1919.*

[31] Included in the minutes of the General Purpose Committee 1930-1948.

[32] Included in the minutes of the General Purpose Committee 1930-1948.